KODÁLY
CHORAL METHOD

44
TWO-PART
EXERCISES

Edited with annotations by

Percy M. Young

Boosey & Hawkes
Music Publishers Limited
London · Paris · Bonn · Johannesburg · Sydney · Toronto · New York

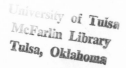

Editor's Introduction

This volume of sight-reading exercises in two parts was first issued in Budapest in 1954, since when it has been extensively and profitably used in the schools of Hungary. In relation to the other volumes of the Choral Method already available in the English edition it is suggested that this collection should be used when those contained in *66 Two-Part Exercises* and *55 Two-Part Exercises* have been mastered. It is strongly urged that the whole sequence of Kodály's exercises in this form (more truthfully they are compositions) should be studied as fundamental to choral practice in the secondary school. The advantages of such study are as follows:

(1) A greater independence in singing is established through the need to concentrate on the presentation of one part against another.

(2) Intonation and rhythm become more accurate when it is understood that miscalculations in these particulars destroy musical coherence.

(3) Consequent on (1) and (2) the essentials of part-singing are grasped through consistent practical experience, and through the steady discipline imposed by a graded course.

(4) This being the case the way is made clear to a great repertoire of unaccompanied vocal music in parts, especially by the great British composers of the age of the madrigal.

(5) When the interplay of separate strands of melody in a musical texture is experienced at first hand the keen pupil will notice how frequent this is in other music, including that for orchestra, to which he may listen, or in the performance of which he may take part.

Individual singers should be encouraged to attempt these pieces as duets. When, however, a class is involved care should be taken to divide it into two groups of equal tonal balance. In both cases preparation is the same. The groups of notes, scales or modes, and the rhythmic structures and patterns should be examined so that the territory covered by each piece is made familiar at once. The teaching notes on pp.3 ff. give such information as may be helpful in this respect. Tempi should be steady, and it is helpful when the teacher conducts. The pupils will learn that the art of corporate music-making depends on an ability to watch the printed music with one eye, the conductor with the other. The singers should also beat the time patterns.

Since confidence is to be engendered the tone should not lie below the level of mezzo-forte. Sight-reading is the art of going on. Singers should not stop if and when errors occur, but always continue to the end of an exercise. Any mistakes can be sorted out afterwards.

Other relevant points will be found in the prefatory matter of the companion volumes of *Choral Method*. I am grateful to Professor Kodály for reading this edition in proof and for suggestions which are incorporated. P.M.Y.

Notes on the Exercises

Each exercise is to be sung in the first place to the solfa syllables, in accordance with the general principles of the Choral Method. In each case the tonic, or key-note, is indicated for both voices at the beginning of the stave. Thereafter a chromatic note occurring in a melody is shown to the appropriate syllable on its first appearance. Except in **46** the composer added no phrase marks. Those shown in all other exercises are editorial and are intended to indicate the structure of the music and also convenient points for breathing. In **44** the dynamics are Kodály's. Otherwise no dynamic markings are given, but this does not mean that the singing should be without dynamic interest: in this respect the singers, or the teacher, should exercise their own judgment, taking into account the general character of each item and the evident contrasts between different pieces. In this way performers will understand that theirs is a creative, not merely a re-creative, function, and that in the interpretation of any work they are partners with the composer. Indications relating to tempo are occasionally given by Kodály by metronome markings; other—editorial—suggestions are placed in brackets and are in no sense to be regarded except as suggestions.

It has been suggested elsewhere that the works of Kodály contained in this series are adaptable for instruments. The pieces in this volume will be found to furnish a welcome addition to the violin duet repertoire, and young players who practise them systematically will enhance their prospects of becoming useful ensemble players. In the few places where the second part lies too low alternative notes are suggested by the editor, although transposition of the parts is to be preferred. Neither singers nor players should be put off by Kodály's occasional omission of bar-lines. This is done to stimulate exactness in interpreting note values.

In studying these pieces with care the singer (or player) is half-way to being a composer in his own right. He may appreciate the importance of tonality in music which is tonal by nature and see how by the insertion of certain chromatic notes variety is introduced. (After *66 Two-Part Exercises* Kodály is more generous with chromatics.) Further points which are apparent are flexibility of rhythm, melodic imitation and a frequent tendency to present material canonically, and effective and controlled use of discord—particularly through passing note and suspension. This series of pieces is a masterly exposition of the art of writing 2-part counterpoint and should be gratefully accepted by all students who either are required or wish to gain fluency in this fundamental technique. It may be said that such students should not merely look at the pieces; they should sing them. The piano is never to be used.

One important lesson to be learned is that music of this relatively simple order need not be without character. It is part of Kodály's greatness that he can turn the simplest material into meaningful music. Each one of these Exercises has its own character. Some are grave and some are gay. But they only become so in fact when interpreted with precision and understanding.

The following detailed notes should be related to those in the earlier volumes since explanations of certain technical points given there are not repeated here.

1 A minor. The subject begins with two leaps, each of a fourth. The lower voice modifies this progression, the first interval now appearing as one of a 5th. This is in accordance with fugal practice, but also "a general principle of developing melodies even among people who never new polyphony" (K.) (Cf. *Bicinia Hungarica* IV). In bar 8 the lower voice enters with the main theme only two beats after the upper voice. This shows the device of *stretto*. N.B. rhythmic details: e.g.

2 E minor. The prevailing interval is the 5th. Notice the strong effect of the intervals of the augmented 4th (lower voice, bar 4) and minor 7th (bar 12). These, and all subsequent intervals encountered for the first time should be carefully measured and *memorised*.

3 E minor. Of playful character. The broken lines between the staves show how two fragmentary parts can make one continuous line of melody.

4 C major. Regarding the entry of the voices and rhythmic details c.f. **1**. The opening pattern of two notes is sometimes shown in inversion.

5 C major. A fugue, with a more or less regular counter-subject. This, marked by the octave leap (lower voice, bar 6) sometimes goes off on its own: note the canonic interlude beginning at bar 10. At bar 24 (upper voice) the melody is inverted.

6 D minor. Bars 25—26 (lower voice) require a cool and calculated approach.

7 D major. The principle of placing four notes against one was embedded in the traditional (and most effective) teaching of counterpoint. Here the strict principle is modified. The singer with long notes has ample time to pay attention to the activities of the other part. This helps good timing. C.f.**9**.

8 D minor. The crotchet coming after a crotchet rest should be felt as springing from the first-beat note in the other part.

9 D minor. C.f. **7**.

10 G major. For treatment of the opening interval c.f. **1**. In the first bar the 7th deserves immediate respect as it occurs frequently later on.

11 E minor. The subject begins with an octave leap, to be developed as a prominent feature of the piece. In bar 32 the lower voice may be grateful to note that the accuracy of the D may (or should) be guaranteed by the upper voice. It is always a good idea to see what help is forthcoming from a contrasting part (c.f. **24**).

12 E minor. In bar 18 *se* (the *leading-note* of the minor scale) goes *up* to *l* in the lower voice: from *l* the melody moves *down* to *la*. Although *se* and *la* are represented by the same note on the piano a string player can show that these are in fact different sounds. The singer should try to realise that there is a difference which is heightened by their functions.

13 E minor. The opening of the subject, taken from Handel, moves from the *dominant* to the *tonic*, through a scale passage. The answer, in the lower part, is modified (c.f. **1**). The second part of the subject, from the end of bar 2, plays a considerable part in the development of the piece.

14 G major. Mark clearly the difference between   and The crotchet should maintain the same value throughout (N.B. bar 3 in triple time, and c.f. *333 Exercises*, **331**, *66 Exercises*, **41**, and *Bicinia Hungarica* I, **34, 35, 36**).

15 C minor. ♫. ♪ = ♫♩♫

16 C minor.

17 F minor.

18 F minor. The interval of the 6th, usually here following that of the 7th, is to be watched with care. In the subject the two lower notes can be felt to make a small but important melodic pattern of their own in contrast to that of the higher notes. Recognising this it is easier to place the sounds (c.f. **20**).

19 D major.

20 A minor. Large intervals to be marked (c.f. **18**). The general pattern of the composition shows four notes against 2 (c.f. **7** and **9**).

21 E minor.

22 Dorian Mode. Although strongly modal the melody is finally pulled into the tonality of A minor by the *cadence*. In this fascinating series of variations (an excellent starting point for young composers) the main melody is rarely lost to view, but it is altered by variations of rhythm and decorations that merit close scrutiny. So also does the division of interest between the parts. A particularly close relationship exists between Variations 4 and 5, 6 and 7, 8 and 9, 10 and 11, 12 and 13, and 14 and 15. In Variation 3 the cross rhythms are easier to adjust when singers (players) think 1 beat in each bar.

23 D minor. The conjoint themes in the opening bars frequently change places, providing excellent examples of *double invertible counterpoint*.

24 B flat major. In bars 23—27 each part helps the other (c.f. **11**).

25 E flat minor. Where there are many accidentals in a key-signature the advantages of sol-fa become even more apparent. Bars 9—10 deserve attention.

26 B flat minor.

27 E flat minor. The more chromatic the music the more expressive it tends to appear. The manner in which the lower voice adds to the expressiveness of this piece is noteworthy. But it will already have become apparent that Kodály thinks of his parts in such music as co-equal.

28 D minor.

29 C sharp minor ⎫
30 F sharp minor ⎬ to be treated lightly and with a nice sense of humour.
31 C sharp minor ⎭

32 G sharp minor.

33 D sharp minor. C.f. **29, 30** and **31**. But here there is a legato phrase to contrast with the staccato notes.

34 D sharp minor.

35 A flat minor.

36 A minor.

37 C major ⎫
38 G major ⎪
39 E major ⎬ Variations on a chromatic scale. C.f. **9** and **11**.
40 F major ⎪
41 D major ⎪
42 D major ⎭

43 a and **b**. A minor. N.B. triplets (c.f. *66 Exercises*, **66**) and in **43b** the chromatic deviation from the route laid down in **43a**.

44 A major.

44 TWO-PART EXERCISES

ZOLTÁN KODÁLY

9

12

16

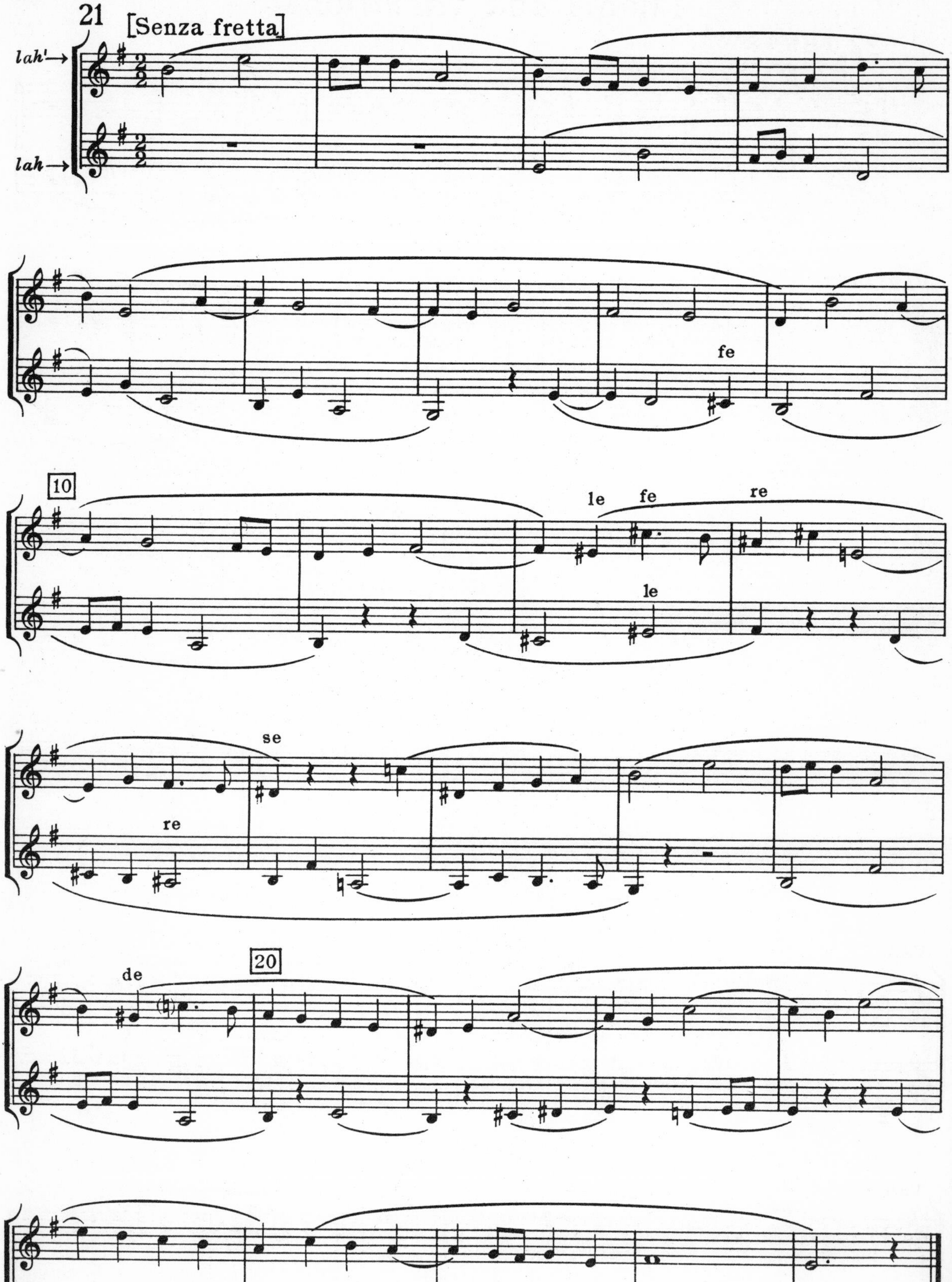
21
[Senza fretta]
lah'
lah
fe
10
le
fe
re
le
se
re
de
20
se

Theme and Variations

28

VAR. 16

VAR. 17 (Finale)

43

B. & H. 19300

43a [Allegretto]

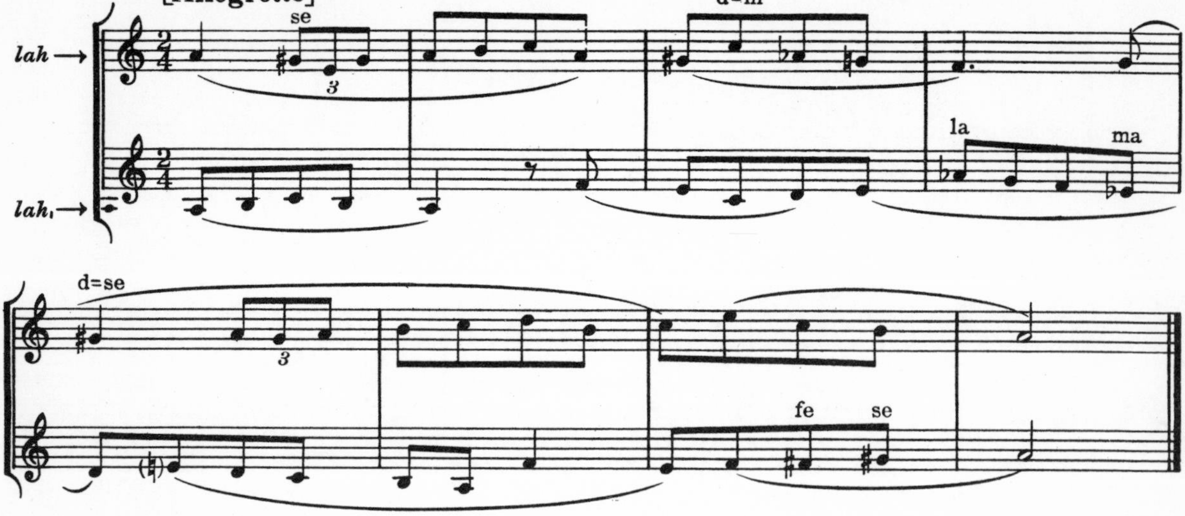

43b [Allegretto]

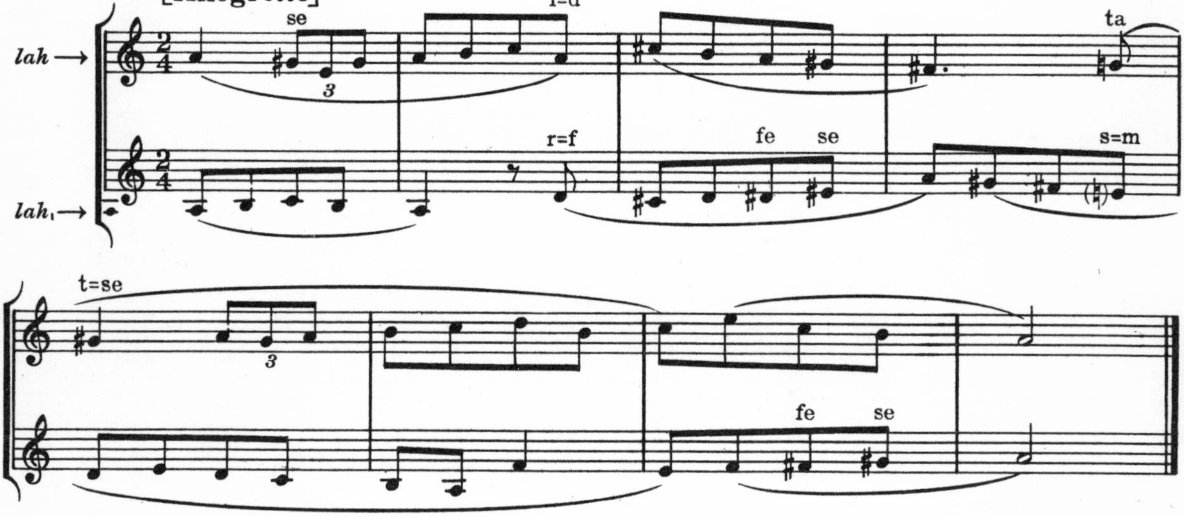

44 [Vivace]

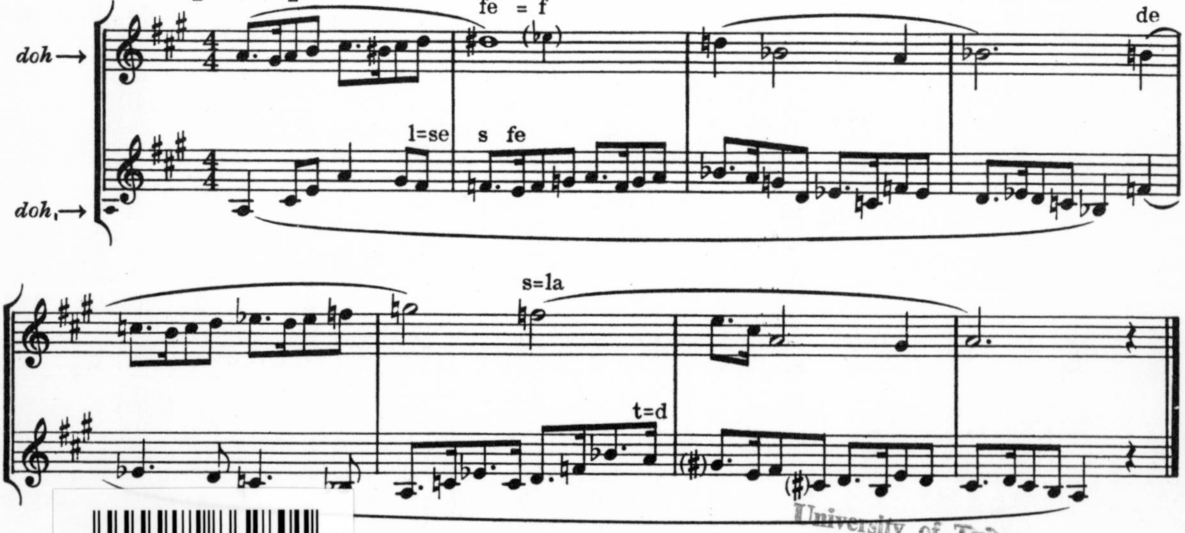

2. 66. E.